Cousins by Adoption

Written by Holly Marlow

Illustrated by Zoe Marlow

ISBN 978-1-7399168-3-1

DEDICATION

For my wonderful nieces. I love you all very much!

ACKNOWLEDGEMENTS

Endless thanks to my wonderful husband Jon, who has supported me in so many ways.
Love you always.

Special thanks to my imaginative superstar, Zoe, for creating the beautiful artwork that
makes this book fun!

My uncle adopted a child last year, so I became a cousin then. It's great! My new cousin and I have so much fun together!

It takes aaaages to adopt a child. My uncle had to wait for months! Don't worry, it's totally worth it!

And it's just a different sort of wait really. Some of my friends had cousins before me, but they had to wait for them to grow in their auntie's tummy and then the baby was tiny and couldn't play for months.

When my uncle adopted my cousin, he was already old enough to play! That was so cool.

My uncle had lots of visits from social workers. They were friendly people, who asked him HUNDREDS of questions, to check he knows how to be a parent properly.

I think he will be brilliant at it, because he's a super fun uncle and he's really good at playing noughts and crosses!

The social workers had to learn all about my uncle, because it's their job to find the exact right family for each child.

My uncle asked me what I thought it would be like to be a cousin. I said I thought he should adopt LOTS of cousins for me to play with!

He said perhaps he would just start with one and see how that goes.

We talked about what it would be like to have to share toys with my new cousin. I told him I'm really good at sharing already, because I share with my friends.

So like I said, it takes aaaaaaaaaaages, but there was a lot to do while my uncle waited for the social workers to find the right child. He got my cousin's room ready while he was waiting.

He got a few toys, so I helped him check that they worked. I was very excited that I would be able to show my cousin how to play with them!

FINALLY, my uncle told me that the social workers had found a little boy who needed a Daddy just like him! I was so excited! He showed me a photo of my new cousin. He looked happy and cheeky!

My uncle couldn't just go and collect my cousin straight away. It's not like shopping, you know. You can't just go and pick up a child. I kind of wished you could. That would have been faster!

My cousin was living with a foster family. Do you know what that is?

Foster families are families who love children and look after them until the social workers find the exact right family for them to live with forever.

My cousin didn't know my uncle yet, so they had some video calls. Then my uncle went to the foster family's house every day for a week to play with my cousin.

When they knew each other a bit better, my cousin came to live with my uncle and to be a part of our family forever.

We waited for a couple of weeks, so that my uncle and cousin could spend some time together, then I finally got to meet my new cousin!

Now he's part of our family forever and we have lots of fun playing and having adventures together!

Suggested Discussion Points

1. How old do you think your new cousin will be when we meet them? What do you think children that age like to do? What kind of toys do you think they will like to play with?

2. How do you feel about sharing and taking turns? Are there some toys that will be harder to share than others when your cousin comes to visit? What shall we do if you don't feel like sharing a toy that's special to you?

3. What do you think social workers think about when they are matching a child to a family? There are lots of things to think about!
    - Some children need to be an only child, (for example if they need a lot of attention because of medical problems,) but others would really like to have a big brother or sister, especially if they had siblings in the foster family.
    - Some children are scared of or allergic to pets, but others would really enjoy having pets in their family.
    - Some children might be used to having one parent, or two parents in the foster family.
    - Some children might have religious or cultural needs.
    - The Social Worker might try to match a child with a family who have the same hobbies and interests.

4. How do you think your cousin will feel when they first meet us? Do you think they will know that we are safe, kind people? What do you think we should do to help them to feel comfortable playing with us?

Also by Holly Marlow

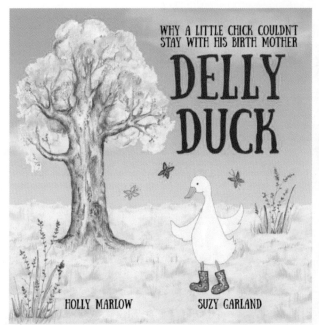

WHY A LITTLE CHICK COULDN'T STAY WITH HIS BIRTH MOTHER

DELLY DUCK

HOLLY MARLOW   SUZY GARLAND

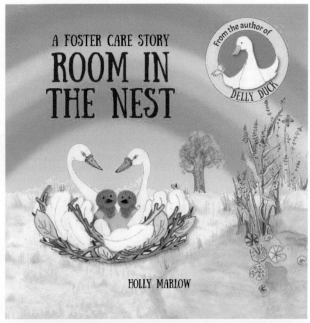

A FOSTER CARE STORY

ROOM IN THE NEST

From the author of DELLY DUCK

HOLLY MARLOW

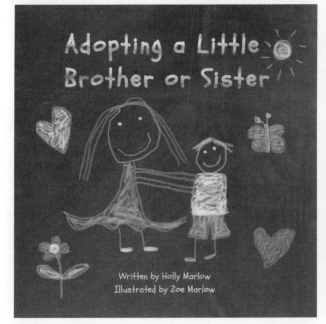

Adopting a Little Brother or Sister

Written by Holly Marlow
Illustrated by Zoe Marlow

So You've Adopted a Sibling

Written by Holly Marlow
Illustrated by Zoe Marlow

About The Author

Holly Marlow is a British author and parent to both biological and adopted children. Holly strives for a gentle/therapeutic parenting style and this has led her to create stories to help children to understand some of the emotional and practical complexities of foster care and adoption.

Holly enjoys travelling (especially searching for chameleons, geckos and snakes in the wild parts of Africa) and learning foreign languages. Holly has fibromyalgia and has spent a lot of time trying to raise awareness of the chronic pain condition, giving presentations in schools and universities. Holly also enjoys baking and gardening, and is terrible at both.

This story is illustrated by Holly's talented daughter, Zoe, who at age 6 enjoys soft play, parks and creating her own illustrated stories and plays. Zoe was eager to provide the illustrations for this book. She created them in less than 10 minutes and has been wondering for months why it took her mother so long to finish the book.

Printed in Great Britain
by Amazon

13022680R00016